June 2009

Welcome to your new life baby boy Espinosa, you are a precious gift from God for your lucky parents to love.

The sky is the limit, the future is yours!

So dream it,
Believe it,
Achieve it!

Hugs & Kisses,

Marie & Cagney

# Animal Friends

# Babies

FOG CITY PRESS

Keeping you close,
your parents
can give you
plenty of kisses.

There are kisses for your brothers and sisters, too.

In a big family, you always have company.

Families share stories
about the day.

Tell me, are you ever scared?

Parents will keep
you safe and
show how to do
new things.

You can do it, if you try!

Let's play hide and seek.

Later, we can have a rumble together.

After playtime, you might be sleepy.

Would you like a cuddle
to go to sleep?

Your parents
love you and like
looking after you.

There is so much to hear.

There are so many places to go.

# Hang on for some new adventures.

# Where would you like to go today?

# Introducing...Your Animal Friends!

 A squirrel monkey and her infant

 A rhinoceros and her calf

 A zebra and her foal

 A giraffe and her calf

 A kangaroo joey

 A squirrel monkey and her infant

 A sea lion and her pup

 A sheep and her lambs

 A goose and her goslings

 A litter of puppies

 A brood of ducklings

 A cat and her kittens

 Five piglets

 A sheep and her lamb

 A horse and her foal

 A cougar cub

 A baby squirrel

 A lion cub on its father's mane

A sheep and her lamb

 A koala and her joey

 A piglet

 A baboon infant and its mother

 A gorilla and her infant

 A cow and her calf

 A panda cub

 A tapir and her calf

 A hippopotamus and her calf

 A fox cub

 A meerkat and her pup

 A vervet monkey infant

 A polar bear and her cub

 A macaque and her infant

 A lemur and her baby

 An orangutan infant

 A baby monkey standing on its mother's head

 A macaque and her infant

 A fox cub

 A baby elephant

Published by Fog City Press,
a division of Weldon Owen Inc.
415 Jackson Street
San Francisco, CA 94111
www.weldonowen.com

**WELDON OWEN GROUP**
Chief Executive Officer  John Owen

**WELDON OWEN INC.**
President, Chief Executive Officer  Terry Newell
Vice President, International Sales  Stuart Laurence
Vice President, Sales and New Business Development  Amy Kar
Vice President, Sales—Asia and Latin America  Dawn Low
Vice President, Publisher  Roger Shaw
Vice President, Creative Director  Gaye Allen
Managing Editor, Fog City Press  Karen Perez
Assistant Editor  Sonia Vallabh
Art Directors  Bret Hansen and Heather Stewart
Designer  Andreas Schueller
Design Assistant  Kevin Yuen
Production Director  Chris Hemesath
Production Manager  Michelle Duggan
Color Manager  Teri Bell

Text  Barbara Vivian Rogers & Albert Wollmer
Picture Research  Ken Perez